£5.99

CONTENTS

Pedigree®

Published by Pedigree Books Limited
The Old Rectory, Matford Lane, Exeter
EX2 4PS.
E-Mail books@pedigreebooks.co.uk
Published in 2001.

THE UNCANNY X-MEN®: Vol. 1, No. 365, March, 1999. (ISSN #1083-401X) Published by MARVEL COMICS. Gerard Calabrese, President. Stan Lee, Publisher. OFFICE OF PUBLICATION: 387 PARK AVENUE SOUTH, NEW YORK, N.Y. 10016. **PERIODICALS POSTAGE PAID AT NEW YORK, N.Y. AND AT ADDITIONAL MAILING OFFICES.** Published monthly. Copyright © 1999 Marvel Characters, Inc. All rights reserved. Price $1.99 per copy in the U.S. and $2.99 in Canada. Subscription rate for 12 issues: U.S. $23.88; foreign $35.88; and Canadian subscribers must add $10.00 for postage and GST. GST #R127032852. No similarity between any of the names, characters, persons, and/or institutions in this magazine with those of any living or dead person or institution is intended, and any such similarity which may exist is purely coincidental. This periodical may not be sold except by authorized dealers and is sold subject to the condition that it shall not be sold or distributed with any part of its cover or markings removed, nor in a mutilated condition. X-MEN (including all prominent characters featured in this issue and the distinctive likenesses thereof) is a trademark of MARVEL CHARACTERS, INC. **POSTMASTER: SEND ADDRESS CHANGES TO THE UNCANNY X-MEN, c/o MARVEL DIRECT MARKETING CORP./SUBSCRIPTION DEPT. P.O. BOX 1979 DANBURY, CT. 06813-1979. TELEPHONE # (203) 743-5331. FAX # (203) 744-9944.** Printed in the U.S.A.

... REMEMBER ME...

NA KOI PES!

... UNLESS YOU CONSIDER THE UNINVITED *POLTERGEIST* IN PETER RASPUTIN'S ROOM AT THE XAVIER INSTITUTE A "CREATURE."

IN THE CHILL OF THE WESTCHESTER WITCHING HOUR, HUMAN SKIN BECOMES MUTANT STEEL --

-- PETER RASPUTIN BECOMES *COLOSSUS* --

... REMEMBER ME, PETER...

-- AND APPARITIONS BECOME *MYSTERIES*.

BUT... I DO KNOW YOU! YOU ARE *HER!* THE WOMAN FROM MY *DRAWINGS!*

WAIT!

COME BACK! I HAVE NOT SEEN YOUR *FACE!* HOW AM I TO *REMEMBER* YOU --

-- HOW AM I SUPPOSED TO *COMPLETE* YOUR IMAGE IF I DON'T KNOW *WHO* --

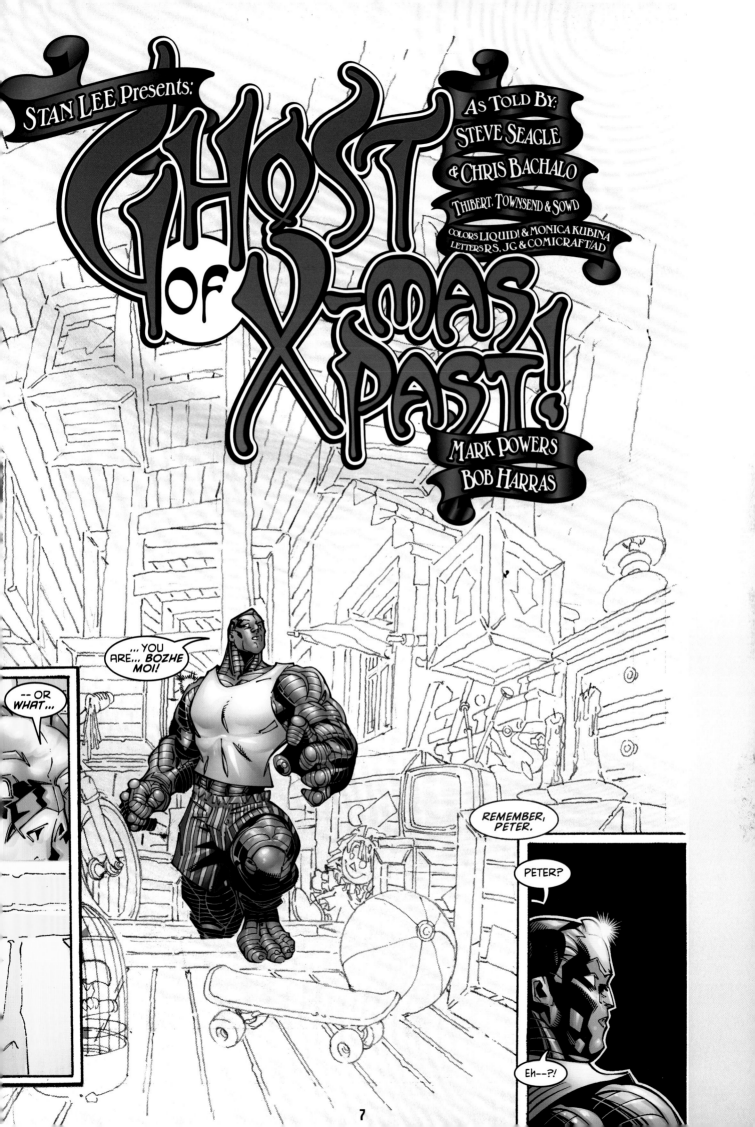

VERY FRIGHTENING INDEED. I CAN SEE WHY YOU WERE SO CONCERNED.

THIS... IS NOT MY DRAWING. I... IT... SOMEONE HAS *TAKEN* THE ORIGINAL CANVAS.

YOU MUST BELIEVE ME, *ORORO.*

I BELIEVE, PETER, THAT YOU BELIEVE YOU SAW SOMETHING.

I ALSO BELIEVE THAT I SAW YOU DRINKING A DOUBLE EXPRESSO FROM THE SALEM CENTER COFFEE BEAN NO MORE THAN AN HOUR BEFORE YOU RETIRED FOR THE EVENING.

MIND AND BODY ARE INTERDEPENDENT. TREAT ONE AS YOU WOULD TREAT THE OTHER AND YOUR NIGHT VISITORS WILL STOP CALLING.

SLEEP WELL, PETER. DO NOT HESITATE TO CALL ME SHOULD YOUR *"PHANTOM"* RETURN.

I... GOOD NIGHT, ORORO.

COULD IT BE? IS MY IMAGINATION RUNNING WILD?

IT HAS BEEN A TIME OF STRESS... RETURNING TO THE MANSION AND BECOMING AN X-MAN ONCE MORE.

PERHAPS I AM HAUNTED BY ONLY THE GHOSTS OF MY OWN *PAST* IN THIS PLACE.

ALTHOUGH THAT DOES NOT EXPLAIN MY *DRAWING* OF THE FACELESS WOMAN. I KNOW I DID NOT DREAM *THAT.*

AND IT COULD NOT HAVE SIMPLY DISAPPEARED. THAT IS NOT LOGICAL.

BUT THEN, NEITHER IS CHASING A *GHOST* THROUGH THE ATTIC.

STILL, WHAT I CREATED *ONCE,* I CAN CREATE AGAIN.

SMASH

EH--?!

SOME-THING IS *OUT* THERE!

LIGHTS AHEAD! AND MORE NOISES AS WELL!

STORM DID NOT BELIEVE ME, BUT I AM NOT ONE TO *IMAGINE* THINGS.

SNAPTK

KRITCH

ONE WOULD THINK THAT AFTER ALL OUR YEARS TOGETHER AS X-MEN --

-- AFTER ALL WE HAVE BEEN THROUGH AND SEEN, SHE WOULD NOT BE SO QUICK TO DOUBT THAT DARK FORCES COULD BE LOOSE ON OUR GROUNDS AND --

SCHLIKT

WHAT'RE YOU DOIN' HERE *THIS* TIME O'NIGHT, PETEY?

I... COULD ASK THE SAME OF *YOU,* WOLVERINE.

HOW QUICKLY THEY FORGET. I *MOVED* OUT HERE WHEN I *GAVE* YOU MY ROOM. *REMEMBER?* NOW BACK TO YOU --

I HEARD NOISES. I CAME TO SEE IF --

BLAME *ME.* I'M THROWING A LITTLE *PARTY.* SINCE YOU'RE UP, COME ON IN.

WELL, WELL, WELL, LOOK WHO DA CAT DONE DRUG IN.

GAMBIT YOU KNOW, AND THOUGH YOU WEREN'T AROUND FOR OUR MOST RECENT POUNDING OF ALPHA FLIGHT --※

-- YOU STILL REMEMBER EUGENE JUDD, THE INFAMOUS PUCK, DON'T YA?

COLOSSUS! LOGAN SAID YOU WERE BACK WITH THE TEAM.

'COURSE HE *ALSO* SAID YOU WAS *SLEEPIN'* SO WHAT DOES *HE* KNOW, EH?

※ THE X-MEN BATTLED A MIND-CONTROLLED ALPHA FLIGHT IN ISSUE 355 -- Mark

10

HOW *ARE* YOU, PUCK? I'M SURPRISED TO SEE YOU HERE.

NOT AS SURPRISED AS THE *BORDER PATROL* WOULD BE, eh? I FORGOT MY I.D., SO I JUST *SNUCK* ACROSS.

DECIDED TO DROP IN ON LOGAN BEFORE I HEADED INTO MANHATTAN.

YOU MIGHT SAY THAT. I THOUGHT I SAW A *GHOST* EARLIER...

...A FEMALE CREATURE OF LIGHT, AND ICE.

GHOST WOMAN? NON, *CAN'T* BE.

SHE SWORE THAT IF *I* STAYED WITH HER, SHE'D LEAVE DE *OTHERS* ALONE.

YOU *OKAY?* YOU'RE LOOKIN' A LITTLE *SHAKY.* WOMAN TROUBLES?

SHE WRAP AROUN' YOU LIKE A SWIRL OF SMOKE?

NO.

SAY SHE WAS IN LOVE WIT' YOU AN' DAT YOU BEST LOVE HER BACK?

NO.

GOOD.

WHY YOU ASKIN', *LeBEAU?* REMIND YOU OF SOME- ONE YOU KNOW?

NOPE.

THEN WHERE YOU GOIN' IN SUCH A HURRY?

THREE'S *COMPANY,* FOUR'S A *CROWD.* BESIDES, I GOT SOME *BUSINESS* TO ATTEND. ⊗

AT 3 A.M? SOUNDS FISHY. I'M GONNA FOLLOW UP ON HIM.

WAIT HERE AND HAVE YOURSELF A *BREW,* PETEY. IT'S ALL THE HOLIDAY CHEER YOU'LL BE GETTIN' FROM *ME.* I DON'T DO CHRISTMAS.

NO, SPASEÉBA. I SHOULD GO BACK IN. ALLOW *ME* TO FOLLOW GAMBIT.

⊗ TO SEE JUST WHAT THAT "BUSINESS" IS, PICK UP *GAMBIT #1* -- ON SALE IN 3 WEEKS! -- Mark

YOU SURE?

YES, BESIDES, I BELIEVE THE CORRECT STATEMENT IS, "*TWO* IS COMPANY. *THREE* IS A CROWD."

11

PERHAPS COMING BACK HERE *WAS* A BAD IDEA.

MAYBE THIS VISION IS TRYING TO REMIND ME WHAT THIS ROAD, BEING AN X-MAN, LED ME TO DURING MY LAST STAY --

-- FALLING UNDER MAGNETO'S SWAY, JOINING THE ACOLYTES, EVEN --

PETER..?

GAHH! AGAIN!

WHY ARE YOU OUTSIDE?

WHY ARE YOU IN MY ROOM? WHAT DO YOU *WANT* FROM ME?

I TOLD YOU, PETER...

...I WANT YOU TO REMEMBER ME...

I WILL NOT BE A VICTIM OF MY OWN INSECURITIES!*

I HAVE RETURNED TO THIS SCHOOL AND MY PLACE IN THE X-MEN BECAUSE I FELT IN MY HEART I SHOULD!

I WILL NOT BE SWAYED BY YOU!

DO YOU HEAR ME, PHANTASM?

WHATEVER IT IS YOU WANT ME TO REMEMBER, YOU WOULD BE WELL-ADVISED TO TELL ME DIRECTLY, OR --

-- OR...

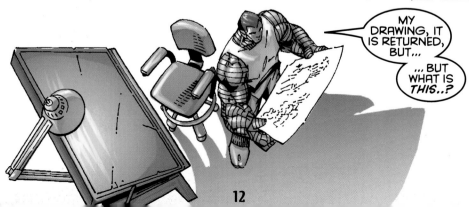

MY DRAWING, IT IS RETURNED, BUT...

...BUT WHAT IS *THIS*..?

THE ICE PRINCESS

Once upon a time... In the lands to the east... Lived The Ice Princess!

She was heir to the wind and the snow and was thought to be the most Beautiful Girl in her empire until... she lost her Face! Her piercing silver eyes, her graceful arching brow, her delicate scarlet lips... all gone with the rise of the morning moon. "But where could it be?!" she shrieked, "A Girl without a Face is a Monster!"

"The King of the Crickets has it!" answered a voice that floated on the frozen air. But as The Ice Princess glanced about, there was no other mouth around. She was completely alone...

IF A SANE MAN'S PEERS FIND HIM *INSANE*, IS IT NOT POSSIBLE THAT *THEY* AND NOT *HE* ARE CORRECT?

PERHAPS *I AM* TIRED. PERHAPS THE STRESS OF MY LIFE HAS FINALLY GOTTEN TO ME. PERHAPS --

...I REMEMBER YOU...

-- THE *VOICE!* THE *LIGHT!*

STOP THIS *TORMENT!*

I KNOW YOU ARE IN HERE!

YES, PETER, I *AM.*

THOUGH HOW THE PRESENCE OF A SCHOOL'S HEADMASTER IN HIS OWN OFFICE COULD BE CONSTRUED AS *"TORMENT"* TO YOU IS *NOT* READILY EVIDENT.

PROFESSOR XAVIER?

YOU LOOK *TROUBLED.* THIS MUST BE A NIGHT FOR BEING ILL AT EASE.

TEA?

NO, THANK YOU. THERE IS A CASE TO BE MADE THAT I HAVE OVER-CAFFEINATED MYSELF ALREADY TONIGHT, THANK YOU.

AND WHAT HAS YOU SO AGITATED?

I AM CONFRONTING TROUBLING GHOSTS.

ON CHRISTMAS EVE? HOW DICKENSIAN. BUT I CAN EMPATHIZE WITH YOU. I AM DOING THE SAME.

YOU... YOU HAVE THEM ALSO?

YES, EVERY YEAR ON THIS DAY, AT ABOUT THIS TIME...

...I MAKE A POINT OF SEEING THEM...

...THOSE WHO HAVE *FALLEN* UNDER MY GUIDANCE.

I LOOK AT THEIR *PHOTOGRAPHS,* I RE-READ THEIR *FILES,* I... *REMEMBER* THEM.

I KEEP THEIR SPIRITS ALIVE IN MY MIND.

SO MANY OF MY STUDENTS TURN OUT LIKE *YOU,* PETER... STRONG, KIND, AND NOBLE...

...BUT THERE ARE THOSE I CANNOT REACH... AND WORSE, THOSE I *CAN,* BUT STILL CANNOT PROTECT FROM *HARM.*

I LIKE TO RECOUNT THEIR ACCOMPLISHMENTS, AND REMIND MYSELF OF WHAT I COULD DO BETTER IF IN A SIMILAR SITUATION IN THE FUTURE.

DO YOU BELIEVE THAT SPIRITS CAN RETURN FROM THE GRAVE?

NOT WITHOUT A *COST.* PLEASE, SIT. I FIND THIS CONVERSATION STRANGELY STIMULATING.

I AM... SORRY, PROFESSOR. BUT I THINK I WILL GO BACK TO MY ROOM. I HAVE... A *DRAWING* TO FINISH.

OH. AS YOU WISH. GOOD NIGHT, THEN.

SUCH A HEAVY WEIGHT TO BEAR.

WE THINK OF THE PROFESSOR AS SO MANY THINGS... LEADER, TEACHER, MENTOR, FATHER...

...HOW EASY IT IS TO FORGET THAT HE TOO IS JUST A MAN WHO MUST DEAL WITH LIFE'S MANY SHOCKS AND --

SURPRISES --!

BY LENIN'S BEARD! *AGAIN?!*

HOW CAN THIS *BE?!*

"Why have you come before me?" chirped the King of the Crickets. And The Ice Princess thought, "I want my face back, and a little voice told me you took it!" But with no mouth to speak, and no voice to sound, she couldn't say that at all.

She moved her arms and waved her hands and shrugged her shoulders. "I don't know what you mean!" said the King. The Ice Princess felt like crying, but with no eyes she couldn't.

Upset, The Ice Princess began to walk away. "You know," called the King of Crickets, "This would all be much easier if you had a face. Perhaps I could give you one of mine." The Ice Princess stopped still. Her frozen heart raced. She turned back to his Highness and thought of a smile.

HEAR ME, SPIRITS! I WILL *NOT* SLEEP THIS NIGHT. I WILL STAY AWAKE FOR THE REST OF *ETERNITY* IF THAT IS WHAT IT WILL TAKE TO GET TO THE BOTTOM OF THIS MYSTERY.

HERE IS ANOTHER IMAGE OF YOUR SO-CALLED *"ICE PRINCESS."*

SKRTCH SKRTCH

I CALL UPON YOU NOW TO COME WRITE UPON IT BEFORE MY EYES!

AND THEN WE WILL SEE WHO IS CRAZY AND WHO IS...

...PETER...?

...EH?

SO YOU HAVE ANSWERED MY CALL? YOU WISH TO TELL ME YOUR STORY?

HERE! HERE IS A NEW PORTRAIT FOR YOU TO DEFACE! WELL? *HAVE AT IT!* THAT IS WHAT YOU WISH, IS IT NOT?

...REMEMBER...

REMEMBER WHO? THE ONLY PERSON YOU RESEMBLE IS... IS...

...YES... REMEMBER ME...

ILL -- ILLYANA...?!

MY... MY *SISTER?!*

SHOW ME YOUR *TORMENTORS!* I WILL DEFEAT *ANY* CREATURE THAT WOULD HARM MY SISTER'S BODY OR SOUL! WHETHER FROM THIS LIFE OR THE ONE AFTER!

MY CONTENTMENT DOESN'T REQUIRE STRENGTH OF *BODY,* IT REQUIRES STRENGTH OF THE *HEART.*

THAT'S THE WAY IT WORKS FOR US SPIRITS. YOU HAVE TO FIGURE IT OUT FOR YOURSELF.

GET THE PICTURE?

...GET... THE... PICTURE...?

PROSTEETYE! YETO MOYA VINA!⊗

⊗ THAT'S RUSSIAN FOR, "FORGIVE ME. IT IS ALL MY FAULT!" -- TRANSLATOR MARK

WHEN MY THINGS WERE DELIVERED FROM MUIR ISLAND, I PACKED THEM *ALL* UP HERE, NEVER OPENING A SINGLE BOX.

I HAD THOUGHT TO START OVER ANEW IN THE MANSION. BUT OF COURSE...

... I SHOULD HAVE NOT LET GO OF *EVERYTHING,* SNOWFLAKE.

EXACTLY, PIOTR. REMEMBER ME. THAT'S ALL I WANTED.

SO IT WAS *YOU* WHO HAS BEEN WRITING THE STORY OF THE ICE PRINCESS ON MY DRAWINGS, ILLYANA? TO TRY AND MAKE ME THINK OF THIS PHOTOGRAPH?

DON'T BE SILLY. GHOSTS CAN'T WRITE.

GOODBYE, MY BROTHER. I'LL ALWAYS BE WITH YOU.

AND I *YOU...*

...BUT THEN WHO...?

23

I MAY NOT KNOW WHO IS GIVING STORY TO MY ART, SNOW-FLAKE --

-- BUT I THINK I DO KNOW WHERE THE FACE OF THE ICE PRINCESS WAS LOST... AND WHAT HER PORTRAIT WAS *MISSING.*

'Twas the night before Christmas...

...and all through the House...

SKRTCH SKRTCH

...Not a Creature was stirring...

...Though some people were still about...

SWP

PETER!

Uh --?!

WE'RE TIRED OF WAITING! COME DOWN ALREADY!

COMING! Uh... JUST A *MOMENT!*

ACH! THERE HE IS! FINALLY!

MERRY CHRISTMAS, SLEEPYHEAD.

THANK YOU, ROGUE. TO *YOU* AS WELL.

ALL OF YOU. I HAVE SOME *GIFTS* FOR YOU, MY PAINTINGS --

-- THEY WERE NOT PURCHASED, BUT THEY ARE OF ME.

I WOULD LIKE EACH OF YOU TO CHOOSE ONE THAT SUITS YOU.

WAIT! ME FIRST! I'VE GOT SOMETHING FOR YOU THAT I DID! WELL... *WE* DID.

I CAN'T DRAW, BUT I WANTED TO SAY *"THANKS"* FOR THAT COOL PICTURE YOU DREW OF ME. ⊗

SO I DECIDED WE COULD COLLABORATE! OPEN IT!

⊗ BACK IN #361.

THANK YOU, I... YOU?!

WE MAKE A GOOD *TEAM*, DON'T WE?

25

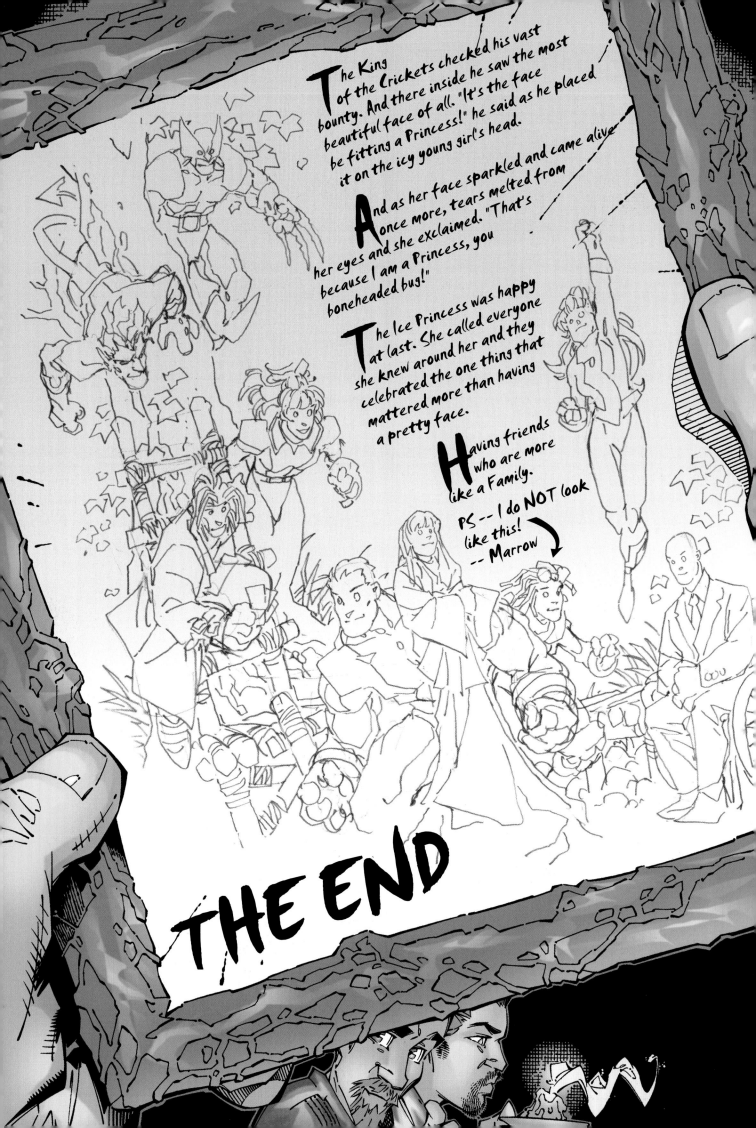

The King of the Crickets checked his vast bounty. And there inside he saw the most beautiful face of all. "It's the face be fitting a Princess!" he said as he placed it on the icy young girl's head.

And as her face sparkled and came alive once more, tears melted from her eyes and she exclaimed. "That's because I am a Princess, you boneheaded bug!"

The Ice Princess was happy at last. She called everyone she knew around her and they celebrated the one thing that mattered more than having a pretty face.

Having friends who are more like a Family.

PS -- I do NOT look like this! -- Marrow

THE END

HAPPINESS IS NO
LAUGHING MATTER
— RICHARD WHATELY

YOU
KNOW
WHAT'S
FUNNY?

PETER PARKER™:SPIDER-MAN®; Vol. 2, No. 20, August, 2000. (ISSN #1053-5667) Published by MARVEL COMICS, Bill Jemas, President; Bob Harras, Editor-in-Chief; Stan Lee, Chairman Emeritus. OFFICE OF PUBLICATION: 387 PARK AVENUE SOUTH, NEW YORK, N.Y. 10016. PERIODICALS POSTAGE PAID AT NEW YORK, N.Y. AND AT ADDITIONAL MAILING OFFICES. Published monthly. Copyright © 2000 Marvel Characters, Inc. All rights reserved. Price $2.25 per copy in the U.S. and $3.50 in Canada. Subscription rate for 12 issues: U.S. $27.00; foreign $39.00; and Canadian subscribers must add $10.00 for postage and GST. GST #R127032852. No similarity between any of the names, characters, persons, and/or institutions in this magazine with those of any living or dead person or institution is intended, and any such similarity which may exist is purely coincidental. This periodical may not be sold except by authorized dealers and is sold subject to the condition that it shall not be sold or distributed with any part of its cover or markings removed, nor in a mutilated condition. PETER PARKER SPIDER-MAN (including all prominent characters featured in this issue and the distinctive likenesses thereof) is a trademark of MARVEL CHARACTERS, INC. POSTMASTER: SEND ADDRESS CHANGES TO SPIDER-MAN, c/o MARVEL DIRECT MARKETING CORP./SUBSCRIPTION DEPT. P.O. BOX 1979 DANBURY, CT. 06813-1979. TELEPHONE # (203) 743-5331. FAX # (203) 744-9944. Printed in the U.S.A. MARVEL COMICS is a division of MARVEL ENTERPRISES, INC. Peter Cuneo, Chief Executive Officer; Avi Arad, Chief Creative Officer.

THINGS ARE GOING TO HAVE TO **CHANGE** FOR ME NOW -- I DON'T KNOW WHAT I'M GOING TO **DO** NOW THAT MJ'S GONE.

BEN PARKER

HE WAS LOVED

WHEN YOU SEE HER, I WANT YOU TO TELL HER I'M **SORRY**, OKAY? I SHOULD'VE BEEN **HONEST** WITH HER... I SHOULD'VE TOLD HER I WAS STILL WEARING THE COSTUME.

"I GUESS I THOUGHT BEING SPIDEY WOULD BE AN **ESCAPE** FOR ME, THE WAY IT USED TO BE. BELIEVE IT OR NOT, SLINGING WEBS AND CATCHING CROOKS ACTUALLY USED TO BE **FUN.**"

DON'T BE SORE, BRAIN. WHEN YOU GET OUTTA THE SLAMMER, YOU CAN ALWAYS FIND WORK AS A **GUMBALL** MACHINE! HAW!

GIFT WRAPPED CROOKS! SPIDEY

HEHH... I GUESS IT'S **EASY** TO LAUGH IN THE FACE OF DANGER WHEN YOU DON'T TAKE **ANYTHING** TOO SERIOUSLY.

I HAVE **YOU** TO THANK FOR THAT, YOU CRAZY OLD GOAT.

"YOU REMEMBER MY FIRST DAY BACK TO SCHOOL THE WEEK AFTER MY PARENTS DIED? THAT DAY, I GOT FREAKED OUT 'CAUSE ALL THE OTHER KIDS WERE WHISPERING AND POINTING AT ME.

"MAN, I WAS SUCH A *NERVOUS* LITTLE DUDE IN THOSE DAYS -- ALL SHORTS AND GLASSES AND ASTHMA. THEY LET ME OFF SCHOOL EARLY 'CAUSE I STARTED CRYING IN GYM CLASS..."

THERE, THERE, PETER... I'LL MAKE US SOME LEMONADE AND YOU'LL BE AS RIGHT AS RAIN IN *NO* TIME, YOU MARK MY WORDS.

"I NEVER REALIZED AT THE TIME, BUT THE OLD HOUSE IN QUEENS USED TO GIVE ME THE *WILLIES* SOMETIMES -- IT WAS ALWAYS SO *QUIET*, EXCEPT FOR THE CREAKING. FOR A LITTLE KID LIKE ME, IT WAS LIKE LIVING IN THE MEDICINE CABINET OF DRACULA."

WHY DON'T YOU GO TELL YOUR UNCLE BEN ABOUT YOUR DAY -- IF YOU ASK *NICELY*, PERHAPS HE'LL GIVE YOU AN ORANGE WEDGE?

"I REMEMBER I USED TO THINK YOU WERE A *GIANT*..."

ERM. UNCA BEN?

YETTHHH?!

WHY, PETER -- WHATEVER'S THE *MATTER*, DEAR?

AUNT MAY! AUNT MAY!

AUHH! UNCA BEN *FRIGHTED* ME!

BEN PARKER! YOU OUGHT TO BE *ASHAMED* OF YOURSELF --

UM. OOH. SORRY, DEAR... I WAS JUST TRYING TO MAKE PETEY LAUGH.

YES, WELL... YOU AND YOUR JOKES GO TOO *FAR* SOMETIMES. YOU KNOW THE BOY HAS A NERVOUS DISPOSITION.

HE'S NOT *LIKE* THE OTHER CHILDREN.

I'M TELLING YOU, MAY, THE BOY'S FINE. HE *NEEDS* A LITTLE TOUGHENING UP --

"WHEN YOU TWO ARGUED, I USED TO FEEL LIKE THE CAT IN THE TOM & JERRY CARTOONS. BUT YOUR FIGHTS NEVER LASTED VERY LONG..."

YOU WEREN'T SCARED, *WERE* YOU, KILLER?

UH-UH... NO *WAY*!

"MAN, THE STUNTS WE PULLED -- IT'S A WONDER AUNT MAY DIDN'T HAVE US BOTH *COMMITTED*."

NOTHING TO REPORT, GENERAL!

"I WONDER IF SHE EVER TUMBLED TO THE FACT THAT YOU'D ALWAYS WANT TO GOOF OFF EVERY TIME WE WERE SUPPOSED TO BE DOING *CHORES*...?"

"AND THEN, REMEMBER ALL THOSE HORRIBLE *JOKES* YOU USED TO TELL? OLD PEOPLE GAGS -- A HUNDRED DIFFERENT VERSIONS OF 'WHY DID THE CHICKEN CROSS THE ROAD?'"

"'T' GET TO THE UVVA *SIDE!*" HAAA HA HA!

"THEY WERE ALWAYS FUNNY, EVERY SINGLE *TIME*.

"YOU TAUGHT ME HOW TO *LAUGH*, I GUESS. AT SCHOOL, I BEGAN TO SEE THE OTHER KIDS DIFFERENTLY. MY SENSE OF HUMOR GOT ME INTO A LOT OF *FIGHTS*...

"...BUT I DIDN'T LOSE *ANY* OF THEM."

OH, GOD... HEHH... IT'S RAINING.

YOU REMEMBER THE OLD *"RAINY DAY"* GAG? THAT WAS A *CLASSIC!* YOU MUST'VE TRIED TO PULL THAT ONE ON ME A HUNDRED TIMES.

BEN PARKER

HE WAS LOVED

"IT ONLY WORKED *ONCE*..."

PETER, IT'S RAINING! COME ON INSIDE... YOU'RE GOING TO GET *WET!*

HA HA! *SEE?* I *TOLD* YOU YOU WERE GOING TO GET WET --

"ON THAT FATEFUL DAY, *WAR* WAS DECLARED...

"THE NEXT AFTERNOON, I WENT DOWN TO THE BIG JOKE STORE IN TOWN AND STOOD IN FRONT OF THE EXPLODING CIGARETTE SECTION FOR, LIKE FIVE OR SIX *HOURS*."

"I WAS *MESMERIZED* BY THE RACKS... SMITTEN WITH DAYDREAMS OF ITCHING POWDER AND FAKE RUBBER SNAKES. IT WAS MY FIRST FORAY INTO THE TWILIGHT WORLD OF *MISCHIEF*."

"I SPENT MY ENTIRE ALLOWANCE IN THAT PLACE, AND I EMERGED WITH VISIONS OF GLORY, AND ENOUGH SNAPPY GUM AND ITCHING POWDER TO STOP THE RED ARMY IN THEIR TRACKS."

"I HAD EVERYTHING I NEEDED FOR MY FIRST MAJOR OFFENSIVE."

"MORE THAN ENOUGH TO TORMENT THE LIFE OUT OF *YOU* FOR THE NEXT HUNDRED YEARS OR SO, ANYWAYS..."

WHY, YOU LITTLE *MONKEY* --

HAAW! HEE --!

"THE WAR OF THE GOOFS WENT ON FOR *YEARS* WITHOUT LETTING UP. OF COURSE, THERE WERE BOUND TO BE *CASUALTIES*..."

UHM... UNCLE BEN -- DON'T YOU WANT TO SIT IN YOUR *FAVORITE* CHAIR? I PUFFED UP THE CUSHION FOR YOU.

"FAVORITE CHAIR," EH? NO THANKS -- I'LL PASS...

OH, MY GOODNESS --

BLARRP

IT WAS *HIM* --!

OMIGOD... THE LOOK ON HER *FACE*. I THINK AFTER THAT WE WERE GROUNDED FOR ABOUT A *YEAR* --

"THE GOOD OLD DAYS," EH, UNCLE BEN?

I DUNNO... MAYBE IT'S ME, BUT DON'T YOU GET THE FEELING THEY'RE GETTING FURTHER AND FURTHER *AWAY*?

BEN PAR

HE WA
LOVED

BUT I'LL TELL YOU ONE THING... YOU TAUGHT ME A PRETTY GOOD *LESSON*. I MEAN, IF IT WASN'T FOR *YOU*, I WOULDN'T HAVE BEEN ABLE TO DEAL WITH WHAT HAPPENED *NEXT* --

"ONE MOMENT, I'M A SKINNY LITTLE GEEK TEENAGER INTO MICROSCOPES AND HAM RADIO AND DOING MY BEST TO AVOID THE SCHOOL FOOTBALL TEAM...

"...THEN ONE DAY, I FEEL THIS TINY LITTLE *BITE* ON MY HAND...

"...AND THEN, WELL... *YOU* KNOW THE REST...

"NEXT THING YOU KNOW, OL' PETE'S A *MILLIONAIRE*. WELL, NOT EXACTLY, BUT I WAS GOING TO BE A STAR OF STAGE AND SCREEN.

"I HAD IT ALL: LOOKS, YOUTH, CHARISMA, SUPER STRENGTH... TEN TONS OF *SPIDER-*SENSE, AND NO COMMON SENSE.

"ONE DAY, AFTER A SHOW, SOME REAL SHIFTY GUY COMES FLYING RIGHT PAST ME, WITH A COP HARD ON HIS HEELS. HE BRUSHES UP NEXT TO ME, CLOSE ENOUGH FOR ME TO GRAB HIM."

I COULD'VE STOPPED HIM WITHOUT A SECOND *THOUGHT*. BUT INSTEAD, I LET HIM *GO*. I DIDN'T EVEN *TRY*.

AND THEN, HE WENT AND *KILLED* YOU.

BEN PARKER

"EVEN AFTER I LOST GWENDY, I KEPT ON TRYING TO FORCE A SMILE. I GUESS I THOUGHT I *HAD* TO -- IT WAS THE ONLY WAY TO KEEP GOING.

"I FACED THE GOBLIN AND I BROUGHT HIM *DOWN*. AND THE WAY I COULD SMILE THROUGH ALL THE PAIN OF IT, THAT MADE IT BEARABLE SOMEHOW.

"BUT NOW, MARY JANE -- MY BEAUTIFUL GIRL, MY WIFE... SHE'S GONE. *FOREVER*."

AN' I... I DIDN'T EVEN GET A CHANCE TO SAY *GOODBYE*.

UNCLE BEN... I DON'T THINK I'M GOING TO BE ABLE TO GO ON *WITHOUT* HER. I KEEP THINKING...

...AH-HUUH... *SNFF*... I KEEP THINKING SHE WOULDN'T HAVE *DIED* IF I'D DONE THINGS *DIFFERENTLY* SOMEHOW.

"AND YOU KNOW WHAT MAKES IT SO *IMPOSSIBLE* NOW? THE BAD GUYS DON'T *CARE* IF I NEED A DAY OFF TO MYSELF. FAST FORWARD TO YESTERDAY AT THE MIDTOWN BANK..."

COME ON -- PUT THE MONEY IN TH' BAGS! *ALL* OF IT! HURRY!

WHATTA YOU *LOOKIN'* AT, GRANDAD? I TOLD YOU TO KEEP YOUR EYES ON THE FLOOR! YOU WANNA PIECE OF THIS --?

OH, *MY* --!

KRASSH

"AND THEN, THERE WAS *ONE*..."

STAY AWAY FROM ME, SPIDER-MAN. I'M WARNIN' YOU -- I'M GONNA BLAST YOU 'WAY! YOU *HEAR* ME?!

I SAID "STAY AWAY." YOU GOTTA BELIEVE ME -- I'LL KILL YOU DEAD, MAN! WHAT'S *WRONG* WIT' YOU --?

OKAY.

I DIDN'T SAY A WORD THE WHOLE TIME. NOT A JOKE OR A PUN OR A WISECRACK. *NOTHING.*

WHAT'S THERE TO SAY WHEN FOR EVERY ONE OF THOSE DIRTBAGS I SEND DOWN, THERE ARE THREE MORE TO REPLACE EACH OF THEM?

I KEPT THINKING, "MAYBE HE'LL SHOOT. MAYBE THEN, IT'LL ALL BE *OVER.*"

BEN PARKER

HE WAS LOVED

SPIDEY USED TO BE MY WAY *OUT,* YOU KNOW? I USED TO GET SUCH A KICK FROM SORTING OUT THE BAD GUYS. BUT NOW... IT'S TOO *MUCH.*

NOW THAT MJ'S GONE, I DON'T *WANT* TO BE A HERO ANYMORE. I JUST WANT TO SEE HER -- JUST FOR A MINUTE -- AND TELL HER I'M *SORRY.*

I MISS HER SO *MUCH,* UNCLE BEN. I KEEP WONDERING TO MYSELF... HOW AM I EVER GOING TO *LAUGH* AGAIN?

HOW'M I GOING TO BE SPIDER-MAN IF I CAN'T *LAUGH?*

BEN PARKER

HE WAS LOVED

SO WHY DON'T YOU TELL ME... 'CAUSE I DON'T *KNOW* ANYMORE.

YOU TELL ME WHAT'S *FUNNY.*

BEN PARKER

HE WAS LOVED

IF THERE'S A *DIFFERENCE* BETWEEN MAN AN' BEAST, BEATS ME WHAT IT *IS*.

AFTER ALL, MAN *STARTED* AS A BEAST.

SURE, THEY SAY MAN EVOLVED A *MORE* ADVANCED BRAIN AROUND THE LIMBIC OR "REPTILIAN" MIND, MAKIN' HIM *MORE* THAN A "MERE" ANIMAL...

BUT THE LIMBIC'S STILL THERE, MAYBE SLEEPIN' AT THE CORE OF WHAT MAN'S BECOME, BUT ALWAYS READY TO AWAKEN--AND IN ME, IT'S A LIGHT SLEEPER, WAKIN' *HARD* AND *FAST*.

I'M A *MUTANT*, MORE EVOLVED THAN THE AVERAGE MAN IN SOME WAYS, MAYBE *LESS* IN OTHERS.

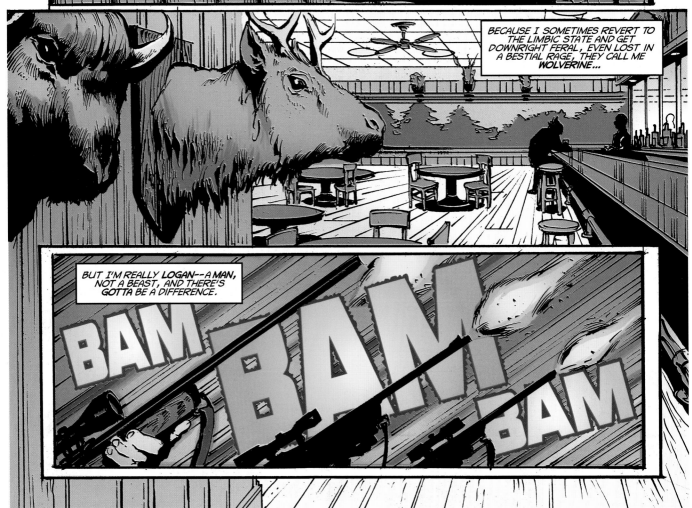

BECAUSE I SOMETIMES REVERT TO THE LIMBIC STATE AND GET DOWNRIGHT FERAL, EVEN LOST IN A BESTIAL RAGE, THEY CALL ME *WOLVERINE*...

BUT I'M REALLY *LOGAN*--A MAN, NOT A BEAST, AND THERE'S *GOTTA* BE A DIFFERENCE.

BAM BAM BAM

53

59

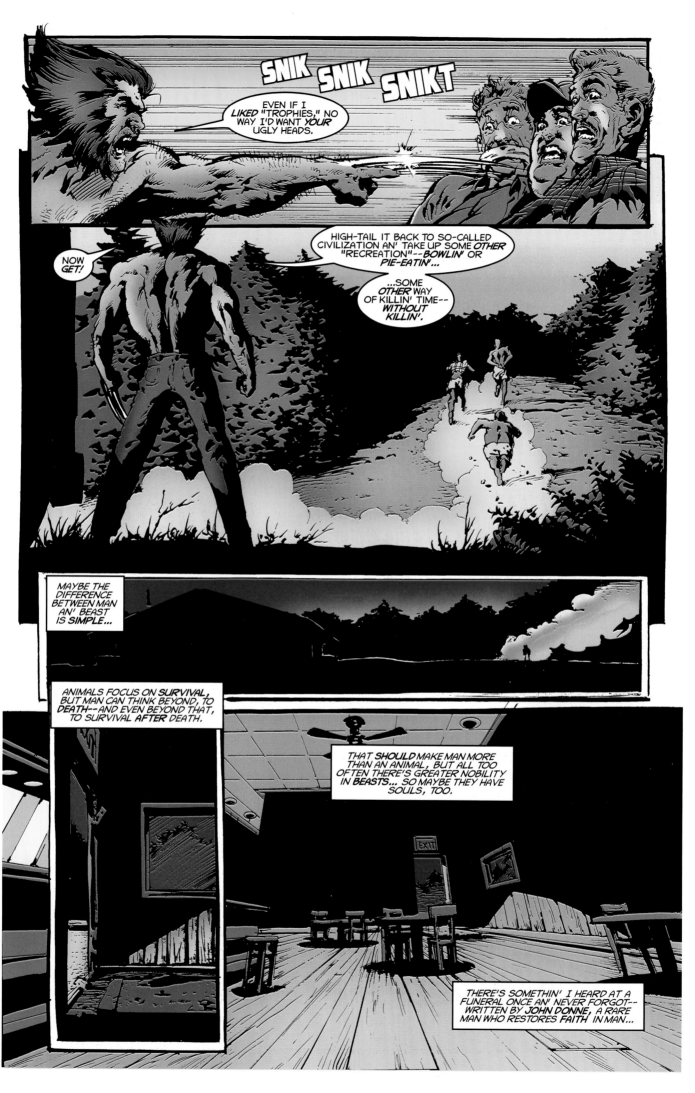

SNIK SNIK SNIKT

EVEN IF I *LIKED* "TROPHIES," NO WAY I'D WANT *YOUR* UGLY HEADS.

NOW *GET!*

HIGH-TAIL IT BACK TO SO-CALLED CIVILIZATION AN' TAKE UP SOME *OTHER* "RECREATION"--*BOWLIN'* OR *PIE-EATIN'*...

...SOME *OTHER* WAY OF KILLIN' TIME-- *WITHOUT KILLIN'.*

MAYBE THE DIFFERENCE BETWEEN MAN AN' BEAST IS *SIMPLE*...

ANIMALS FOCUS ON *SURVIVAL*, BUT MAN CAN THINK BEYOND, TO *DEATH*--AND EVEN BEYOND THAT, TO SURVIVAL *AFTER* DEATH.

THAT *SHOULD* MAKE MAN MORE THAN AN ANIMAL, BUT ALL TOO OFTEN THERE'S GREATER NOBILITY IN *BEASTS*... SO MAYBE THEY HAVE SOULS, TOO.

THERE'S SOMETHIN' I HEARD AT A FUNERAL ONCE AN' NEVER FORGOT-- WRITTEN BY *JOHN DONNE*, A RARE MAN WHO RESTORES *FAITH* IN MAN...